山姆的脚印格子

【美】纳特·盖布里埃尔◎著

【美】罗恩·弗里茨◎绘

袁　颖◎译

天津出版传媒集团

新蕾出版社

图书在版编目 (CIP) 数据

山姆的脚印格子/(美)盖布里埃尔(Gabriel,N.)
著;(美)弗里茨(Fritz,R.)绘;袁颖译.—天津:
新蕾出版社,2015.3(2024.12 重印)
(数学帮帮忙·互动版)
书名原文:Sam's Sneaker Squares
ISBN 978-7-5307-6210-3

Ⅰ.①山…　Ⅱ.①盖…②弗…③袁…　Ⅲ.①数学−
儿童读物　Ⅳ.①01−49

中国版本图书馆 CIP 数据核字(2015)第 037037 号

Sam´s Sneaker Squares by Nat Gabriel;
Illustrated by Ron Fritz.
Copyright © 2002 by Kane Press, Inc.
All rights reserved, including the right of reproduction in whole or in part in any
form. This edition published by arrangement with Kane Press, Inc. New York, NY,
represented by Lerner Publishing Group through The ChoiceMaker Korea Co.
agency.
Simplified Chinese translation copyright © 2015 by New Buds Publishing House
(Tianjin) Limited Company
ALL RIGHTS RESERVED
本书中文简体版专有出版权经由中华版权代理中心授予新蕾出版社(天津)有
限公司。未经许可,不得以任何方式复制或抄袭本书的任何部分。
津图登字:02−2012−229

出版发行:天津出版传媒集团
　　　　　新蕾出版社
http://www.newbuds.com.cn
地　　址:天津市和平区西康路 35 号(300051)
出 版 人:马玉秀
电　　话:总编办 (022)23332422
　　　　　发行部 (022)23332679　23332351
传　　真:(022)23332422
经　　销:全国新华书店
印　　刷:天津新华印务有限公司
开　　本:787mm×1092mm　1/16
印　　张:3
版　　次:2015 年 3 月第 1 版　2024 年 12 月第 23 次印刷
定　　价:12.00 元

无处不在的数学

资深编辑 卢 江

　　人们常说"兴趣是最好的老师",有了兴趣,学习就会变得轻松愉快。数学对于孩子来说或许有些难,因为比起语文,数学显得枯燥、抽象,不容易理解,孩子往往不那么喜欢。可许多家长都知道,学数学对于孩子的成长和今后的生活有多么重要。不仅数学知识很有用,学习数学过程中获得的数学思想和方法更会影响孩子的一生,因为数学素养是构成人基本素质的一个重要因素。但是,怎样才能让孩子对数学产生兴趣呢?怎样才能激发他们兴致勃勃地去探索数学问题呢?我认为,让孩子读些有趣的书或许是不错的选择。读了这套"数学帮帮忙",我立刻产生了想把它们推荐给教师和家长朋友们的愿望,因为这真是一套会让孩子爱上数学的好书!

　　这套有趣的图书从美国引进,原出版者是美国资深教育专家。每本书讲述一个孩子们生活中的故事,由故事中出现的问题自然地引入一个数学知识,然后通过运用数学知识解决问题。比如,从帮助外婆整理散落的纽扣引出分类,从为小狗记录藏骨头的地点引出空间方位等等。故事素材全部来源于孩子们的真实生活，不是童话，不是幻想，而是鲜活的生活实例。正是这些发生在孩子身边的故事，让孩子们懂得，数学无处不在并且非常有用；这些鲜活的实例也使得抽象的概念更易于理解，更容易激发孩子学习数学的兴趣，让他们逐渐爱上数学。这样的教育思想和方法与我国近年来提倡的数学教育理念是十分吻合的！

　　这是一套适合5~8岁孩子阅读的书，书中的有趣情节和生动的插画可以将抽象的数学问题直观化、形象化，为孩子的思维活动提供具体形象的支持。如果亲子共读的话，家长可以带领孩子推测情节的发展，探讨解决难题的办法，让孩子在愉悦的氛围中学到知识和方法。

　　值得教师和家长朋友们注意的是，在每本书的后面，出版者还加入了"互动课堂"及"互动练习"，一方面通过一些精心设计的活动让孩子巩固新学到的数学知识，进一步体会知识的含义和实际应用；另一方面帮助家长指导孩子阅读，体会故事中数学之外的道理，逐步提升孩子的阅读理解能力。

　　我相信孩子读过这套书后一定会明白，原来，数学不是烦恼，不是包袱，数学真能帮大忙！

我本以为修剪草坪不是什么难事呢。第一块还算顺利，可第二块似乎总也干不完！我却必须得把它修剪完，否则，我就得不到报酬。没有钱就意味着我的新自行车就要泡汤。

3

"噢，山姆！我刚擦完的地板！"妈妈叫道。

我低头一看，"哎哟，对不起，妈妈。我忘记把脚弄干净再进来了。"

"让我猜猜。"哥哥戴夫说，"你脑子想别的事了吧？也许飘到了另外一个星球。"

"别逗弟弟了，戴夫。"妈妈说，"他没办法停止思考，因为……"

"他是个深奥的思想家。"戴夫说。

"没错。"妈妈说，"世界正需要像我们山姆这样深奥的思想家呢。"

哥哥翻了个白眼。

5

"那么，你刚才在想什么呢，宝贝？"妈妈问。

"希尔先生家的后院。"我回答道。

"哦，那可真是够深奥的。"戴夫说。

"你觉得它比格林太太家的院子大出多少呢？"我问他。

“你关心这个干什么？”戴夫问。

“因为修剪希尔先生家的草坪比修剪格林太太家的草坪多费好长时间。”我说，“我跟希尔先生说了，可他说我可能是因为没喝饱牛奶什么的觉得累了而已。”

"我敢肯定,他家的草坪就是比格林太太家的大多了。"我说,"真希望我能证明这一点。这样他也许会多付我一些报酬。"

　　"我能教你怎么办。"戴夫说。

　　"太好了。"我说,"那……我们怎么做?"

　　"我有什么好处呢?"戴夫问道。

　　"我帮你刷一个星期的碗!"我主动表示。

戴夫在他的餐巾纸上画了一个长方形。"假设这是一块草坪。"他说,"你量量这两个边长——长和宽,然后,把它等分成大小一样的方格,就像这样。"

　　"然后呢?"我问。
　　"你把这些格子数一数。格子越多,面积越大啊。"
　　"你的意思是草坪就越大?"我问。
　　"你说对了!"戴夫说。

我有点儿明白又不太明白。我该怎么去丈量草坪呢？就用一把小尺子吗？那永远也量不完！

　　"可我怎么才能……"我说道。这时传来了
口哨声，戴夫抓起他的外套奔向门口。

　　"我走了。"他说。

　　"等等！"我边喊边起身追了出去。

　　"站住，山姆！我的地板啊！看看这些脚印！"
妈妈大喊。

　　我光忙着抓住戴夫问个明白，把自己穿着一
双泥球鞋的事全忘到脑后去了。我看着那些脚
印，突然计上心来。

　　"妈妈,您是个天才!"我说道,"您说得没错。
我要做的,就是看看地板啊!"
　　妈妈挠挠头,转身拿拖把去了。

我脱下球鞋，赶忙跑进自己的房间。

"假设这块地毯就是格林太太家的草坪。"
我自言自语道。我开始沿着地毯的长边走，正
好 6 脚。

　　然后我转过身，沿着地毯的短边走，3脚。
这块地毯长6脚，宽3脚。

"你到底在干什么呢，山姆？"妈妈在楼下喊道，"你的脚步像头大象。"

　　"我在丈量格林太太家的草坪！"我回答。

　　妈妈没答话，可我听见她上楼来了。

我在一张纸上画下一个长方形。在长的一边上画下 6 个脚印,跟我踩在妈妈刚擦过的地板上的一样。然后,我在短的一边上画下 3 个脚印。

18 个脚印格

　　我把整个长方形划分成等大的正方形格子。脚印格子，我决定这么给它们命名。

　　"你刚刚在说，你在丈量草坪？"妈妈问。

　　"对呀，有 18 个脚印格子那么大。"我回答，"很棒吧？"

整整一天，我都在练习丈量。我量了起居室。爸爸还算镇定。

我量了储藏室。当我全都搞定时，妈妈看上去挺高兴的。

20

我把家里每个房间都量了个遍。天哪，量来量去搞得我饥肠辘辘、筋疲力尽。我简单吃了点儿，打了个盹儿。你猜怎么着？

我梦见的全是脚印格子！每到一处，大家都让我量东西。

　　"量下停车坪，山姆！"

　　"量下球场，山姆！"

　　"不，山姆。量量我！"我听见身后传来一个奇怪的声音。

我转过身。那儿站着一个巨型的花生酱果冻三明治。它笑着，开始追着我满屋子跑，嘴里还喊着："山姆！山姆！"

　　我睁开眼睛。哟！是妈妈在喊我，不是什么三明治。

我该到格林太太家修剪草坪了。我用最快的速度跑到那里。但在动工修剪之前，我要先丈量。她家的草坪 20 脚长，10 脚宽。哇！太容易了。我画了方格图，然后 10 个 10 个地数。

　　"您的草坪正好有 200 个脚印格子那么大。"
我说。

　　"很好，亲爱的。"格林太太说。

　　她付给我报酬后，我奔向希尔先生家。

　　"我觉得早上修剪过之后,这草还没得空儿再长呢。"希尔先生冲我喊道,"下周再过来吧,好吗?"

　　"我不是来修剪草坪的,我是来丈量的。"我解释道。

"1，2，3，4……"我一边数着，一边在草坪边上用脚印丈量。

"看起来很有趣啊，需要我帮忙吗？"希尔先生问道。

"不用了，谢谢。"我说，"您的脚比我的大。您的鞋印也会比我的大得多啊。"

希尔先生脸上的表情跟妈妈经常流露出的表情一模一样。

丈量结束,我向希尔先生宣布结果。

"之所以修剪您的院子要花上更长的时间,是因为它比格林太太家的草坪要大上 160 个脚印格子。"我告诉他。

“你肯定吗？”他问。

　　“我肯定。”我说，“所以您得付我更多的
报酬。”

　　“应该的。”他说，“可我还是觉得你得多
喝点儿牛奶。”

离开了希尔先生家,我突然又想起来:哇! 要是我能找到更大面积的草坪来修剪，我就可以挣到更多的钱了。那自行车很快就是我的了!

　　我已经等不及要把我的想法公之于众了。我一溜烟儿跑回了家。

"猜猜我要干什么？"我说。

"不知道。"妈妈说，"可我知道你又忘了什么。"

"天哪！"我叫道，低头看着脚下的地板，"对不起，妈妈！但是，还是先听听这个吧！"

31

面积图

物体的表面或封闭图形的大小，叫作它们的面积。

面积的国际标准单位是平方米。

山姆说，如果 ■ 叫 1 平方单位的话，那么下面每一个图形的面积都是 36 平方单位。他说得对吗？

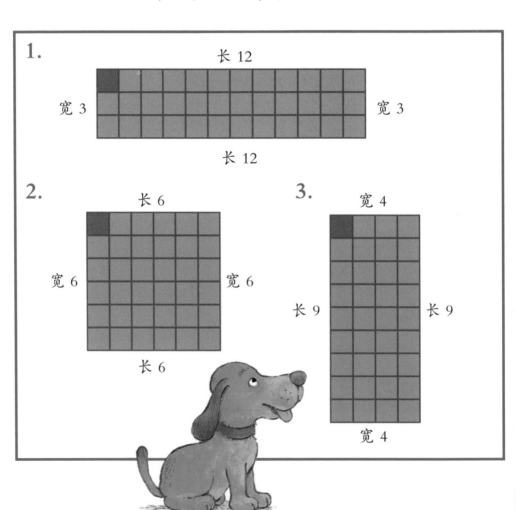

1.

宽 3　　长 12　　宽 3

长 12

2.

宽 6　　长 6　　宽 6

长 6

3.

长 9　　宽 4　　长 9

宽 4

亲爱的家长朋友，请您和孩子一起完成下面这些内容，会有更大的收获哟！

提高阅读能力

• 看看封面，读读标题。让孩子猜猜看，山姆正在便签本上写什么呢？

• 读过故事，让孩子说说，为什么山姆决定比一比希尔先生家和格林太太家的草坪哪个大？为什么山姆帮希尔先生锄草后，希尔先生多付了钱给山姆？山姆是怎么让希尔先生相信他的说法的？

• 什么东西让山姆想到了测量草坪的办法？

（参见第 12～13 页）

巩固数学概念

● 利用第 32 页的图表，理解"面积"和"平方单位"的意思。引导孩子用每个概念造个句子。

● 观察第 32 页图表中的图形。哪个图形最长？哪个图形最宽？帮助孩子验证这三个图形的面积是一样的。

● 每一块草坪中各有多少个脚印格子？（参见第 28 页）提示孩子可以"跳着数"，快速数清格子的数量。格林太太家的草坪有 20 脚长，10 脚宽。10 个 10 个地数，她家的草坪有 200 个脚印格子。用同样的方法数，希尔先生家的草坪有 360 个脚印格子。教给孩子另一种计算方式——乘法：$20 \times 10 = 200$，$20 \times 18 = 360$。鼓励孩子两种方式都试一下。

● 计量的工具常常是尺子。故事中，山姆用的计量工具是什么？第 27 页里，希尔先生想要帮忙一起量，为什么被山姆婉言谢绝了？

生活中的数学

● 让孩子用自己的脚印去丈量面积并比较大小，看看哪一块地方更大。可以参照山姆的方法。（参见第 14~17 页）

● 给孩子提供物件或纸张，让孩子自己围成或绘出不同形状的地面图形，并描述一下每块地方适合做什么用，比如游戏室、卧室、教室等。

上面的四个图形中，哪个面积最大？哪个面积最小？

小小设计师

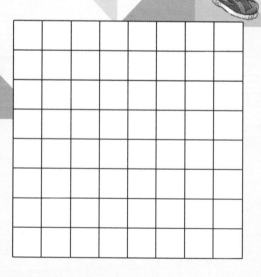

我设计了 2 个图案，每个图案的面积都是 4 个 □。你是否也能设计出同样面积大小的图案呢？

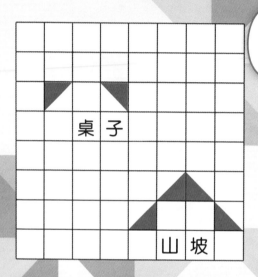

桌 子

山 坡

请你来当图案设计师！

如果给下面的这块地板铺瓷砖，一共需要多少块？你能算出来吗？

如果请人整理左边的这块草地需要付 16 元,那么整理下面的草地需要付多少元?

写出下面图形的面积。

图①的面积是(　　　　)平方单位。

图②的面积是(　　　　)平方单位。

动动小脑筋

①生活中常用的面积单位有哪些？你能列举几个吗？

②开动脑筋想一想，有什么方法能够测量一下你家里客厅的大小？请把它记录下来。

互动练习1：

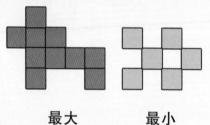

最大　　　　　最小

互动练习2：
略

互动练习3：
36块

互动练习4：

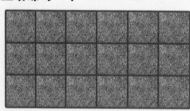

18元

互动练习5：

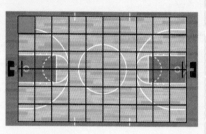

60平方单位

互动练习6：

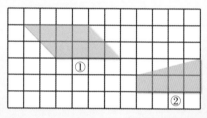

① 8平方单位
② 6平方单位

互动练习7：
①平方厘米、平方分米、平方米……
②略

（习题设计：董惠平　王　康）

42

Sam's Sneaker Squares

I thought mowing lawns would be easy.

The first one was. But the next one seemed to take forever! I had to finish it, though. Otherwise I wouldn't get paid. And no money would mean no new bike.

"Oh, Sam! I just washed the floor!" said Mom.

I looked down. "Whoops. sorry, Mom. I forgot to wipe my feet."

"Let me guess," said my older brother, Dave. "Was your mind somewhere else? Like on another planet maybe?"

"Don't tease your brother, Dave," said Mom. "He can't help it because—"

"He's a deep thinker," said Dave.

"That's right," Mom said. "The world needs deep thinkers like our Sam."

My brother rolled his eyes.

"So, what were you thinkng about, honey? " Mom asked.

"Mr. Hill's backyard," I said.

"Wow, that's deep all right," said Dave.

"How much bigger do you think it is than Mrs. Green's yard? " I asked him.

"Why do you care?" Dave said.

43

"Because it took a lot longer to mow his lawn than hers," I said. "I told Mr. Hill that, but he said I was probably just tired from not drinking enough milk or something."

"I'm sure his lawn is a lot bigger than hers," I said. "I wish I could prove it. Then maybe he'd pay me more."

"I could show you how," said Dave.

"Great," I said. "So... how?"

"What's in it for me?" Dave asked.

"I'll clear your dishes for a week," I offered.

Dave drew a rectangle on his napkin. "Say this is a lawn," he said. "You measure the two sides—the length and width. Then you divide it into equal squares—like this."

"Then what?" I asked.

"You count up all the squares. The more squares, the bigger the area."

"You mean the bigger the lawn?" I asked.

"You've got it!" said Dave.

I sort of got it and sort of didn't. How was I supposed to measure the lawn? With a ruler? That would take forever.

"But how am I supposed to—" I said. Just then a horn honked. Dave grabbed his jacket and headed out the door.

"Gotta go," he said.

"Wait!" I yelled, starting to run after him.

"Stop, Sam! My floor! Just look at it!" cried Mom.

I'd been so busy talking to Dave, I'd forgotten all about my muddy sneakers. I looked at the footprints. And that's when it hit me.

"Mom, you're a genius," I said. "You were right. All I needed to do was just look at the floor."

Mom scratched her head and went to get the mop.

I took off my sneakers and hurried up to my room.

"Let's say this rug is Mrs. Green's lawn," I said to myself. I started walking down the long side of the rug. It took six steps to get across.

Then I turned and started walking down the short side of the rug. Three steps. Six steps across and three steps down.

"What on earth are you doing, Sam?" Mom called from downstairs. "You sound like an elephant."

"I'm measuring Mrs. Green's lawn!" I called back.

Mom didn't answer, but I heard her start coming up the stairs.

On a piece of paper I drew a rectangle. I drew six sneaker prints on one side, like the ones I'd made on Mom's clean floor. Then I put three more prints along the other side.

I divided the whole thing into squares. Sneaker squares, I decided to call them.

"Did you say you're measuring a lawn?" Mom said.

"Yeah, and it's 18 sneaker squares big," I said. "Isn't that cool?"

All day I practiced measuring. I measured the living room. Dad wasn't too thrilled.

I measured the den. Mom seemed glad when I was all done.

I measured every room in the house. Boy, all that measuring made me hungry and tired. So I had a snack. Then I took a nap. Guess what?

I dreamed about sneaker squares! Everywhere I went people kept asking me to measure things.

"The parking lot, Sam!"

"The football field, Sam!"

"No, Sam. Measure ME!" I heard a strange voice behind me say.

I turned around. There stood a giant peanut butter and jelly sandwich. It smiled and began to chase me around the room, yelling—

"Sam! Sam!"

I opened my eyes. Whew! It was only my mother calling me, not a sandwich.

I was supposed to be at Mrs. Green's house mowing her lawn. I ran over there as fast as I could. But before I started mowing, I measured. Her lawn was twenty steps long and ten steps wide. Wow! This was easy. I made a grid and counted by tens.

"Your lawn is exactly 200 sneaker squares big," I said.

"That's nice, dear," said Mrs. Green.

She paid me, and I headed over to Mr. Hill's house.

"I don't think the grass has had a chance to grow much since this morning," Mr. Hill called out. "Come back next week, okay?"

"I'm not here to mow, I'm here to measure," explained.

"One, two, three, four—" I said, taking sneaker steps along the edges of the yard.

"That looks like fun. Can I help?" asked Mr. Hill.

"No, thanks," I said. "Your feet are longer than mine. Your sneaker steps would be way too big."

Mr. Hill gave me that same look my mother always does.

When I had finished measuring, I gave Mr. Hill the news.

"The reason your yard takes longer to mow is that it's 160 sneaker squares bigger than Mrs. Green's," I told him.

"Are you sure?" he asked.

"I'm positive," I said. "So I'll have to charge you more."

"That's fair," he said. "But I still think you should drink more milk."

After I left Mr. Hill's, it hit me. "Wow," I thought. "If I can find even bigger lawns to mow, I can earn a lot more money. That bike could be mine in no time at all!"

I couldn't wait to tell everybody my idea. I ran all the way home.

"Guess what I'm going to do?" I said.

"I don't know," said my mother. "But I know what you forgot to do."

"Whoops!" I said, looking down at the floor. "I'm sorry, Mom! But wait till you hear this!"